Spelling for Literacy

for ages 8–9

Suggestions for using this book...

We have examined carefully the current national policies for teaching spelling as part of your literacy work. In writing this book we have incorporated word lists for every spelling objective in the Literacy Strategy, in addition to all the medium frequency words suggested for this year group. We have arranged the words into sets, usually of sixteen words. Many of the activity sheets are designed to aid the development of the pupils' dictionary skills. Each set of words is used in three styles of sheet:

Sheet A

✓ Can be photocopied onto OHP transparencies for discussion.

✓ Can be displayed on the wall as 'Words of the Week'.

✓ Can be copied onto card and cut up to make matching cards.

Sheet B

✓ Activity sheets to be used in the Literacy Hour.

✓ Can be hole-punched to go in pupils' personal spelling files.

✓ Can be given as homework sheets.

✓ **Answers provided on the last three pages of this book.**

Sheet C

✓ Has a fold line so that children can copy the words, then cover them to write again without looking.

✓ A perfect follow-up activity for the learning which has taken place using sheets A and B.

✓ Following the Learn, Write, Check system.

Spelling for Literacy *for ages 8-9*

Contents

The variety of words provided for Year 4 Term 1 is enormous, ranging from words such as **go** and **went** to much more challenging words such as **government** and **championship**. The harder words present great opportunities for extending pupils' vocabulary within their written work. <u>All</u> of the words provide opportunities for discussion and we recommend that you use Sheet A in each set, as a focus for pointing out patterns. Many children will need guidance in seeing relationships such as those found in Set 5, for example. Examining and discussing the word **craftsmanship** by considering first **craft**, then **craftsman**, then **craftsmanship**, can help children to gain skills in spelling which are transferable to other words.

Set 1 Sheets A, B & C	Year 4 Term 1 Suffixes: ment, ness	sadness, kindness, silliness, happiness, drowsiness, darkness, softness, hardness, agreement, appointment, merriment, enjoyment, entertainment, engagement, government, endearment
Set 2 Sheets A, B & C	Year 4 Term 1 Suffixes: ic, al, ary	music, magic, picnic, logic, fantastic, library, canary, dictionary, contrary, literary, medical, hospital, mystical, chemical, seasonal, traditional
Set 3 Sheets A, B & C	Year 4 Term 1 Double consonants	kettle, kitten, dinner, riddle, little, woollen, better, mirror, middle, bubble, rubble, summer, batter, tatter, tomorrow, scrabble
Set 4 Sheets A, B & C	Year 4 Term 1 Homophones ✓ 11/11/12	to, two, too, there, they're, their, night, knight, pear, pair, ate, eight, stare, stair, see, sea
Set 5 Sheets A, B & C	Year 4 Term 1 Suffixes: ship, hood	brotherhood, knighthood, livelihood, neighbourhood, childhood, falsehood, friendship, membership, relationship, hardship, companionship, partnership, workmanship, craftsmanship, championship, ownership
Set 6 Sheets A, B & C	Year 4 Term 1 Regular verb endings	look, looks, looked, looking, stay, stays, stayed, staying, rush, rushes, rushed, rushing, wash, washes, washed, washing
Set 7 Sheets A, B & C	Year 4 Term 1 Regular verb endings	stop, stopped, drag, dragged, hop, hopping, skip, skipping, carry, carries, carried, carrying, fry, fries, fried, frying
Set 8 Sheets A, B & C	Year 4 Term 1 Irregular tense changes	go, went, buy, bought, bring,brought, eat, ate, run, ran, write, wrote, think, thought, fling, flung
Set 9 Sheets A, B & C	Year 4 Term 1 Irregular tense changes	shoot, shot, catch, caught, fight,fought, hear, heard, shake, shook, wear, wore, creep, crept, break, broke
Set 10 Sheets A, B & C	Year 4 Term 1 Nouns and adjectives into verbs	special, specialise, theory, theorise, personal, personalise, apology, apologise, note, notify, jolly, jollify, beauty, beautify, pure, purify
Set 11 Sheets A, B & C	Year 4 Term 1 Nouns and adjectives into verbs	flat, flatten, sweet, sweeten, tough, toughen, weak, weaken, awake, awaken, alien, alienate, elastic, elasticate, medicine, medicate
Set 12 Sheets A, B & C	Year 4 Term 1 Verb endings	meet, meets, met, meeting, run, runs, ran, running, jump, jumps, jumping, jumped, go, goes, going, gone
Set 13 Sheets A, B & C	Year 4 Term 1 Revision of Term 1	amble, ambled, saunter, sauntered, hair, hare, blue, blew, tell, told, pedal, appointment, library, neighbourhood, do , does

Spelling for Literacy *for ages 8-9*

Contents

Ten sets of words are provided for Year 4 Term 2, reflecting the fact that this is generally a shorter term. We recommend photocopying Sheet A for each set, either as an overhead projector transparency or as a sheet to be pinned up for discussion.

It is essential that the children have the opportunity to discuss the words, identifying similarities and differences in patterns and structures. In examining Set 14, for example, they could be encouraged to realise that the first fourteen words are all nouns, whereas **safe** is an adjective and **saves** is a verb - despite the difference in the word function, however, the spelling pattern is the same as in the words **life** and **lives**, where the singular noun changes its ending to become a plural.

Set 14 Sheets A, B & C	Year 4 Term 2 Word endings: f, fe, ff	calf, calves, half, halves, self, selves, cliff, cliffs, sniff, sniffs, knife, knives, life, lives, safe, saves
Set 15 Sheets A, B & C	Year 4 Term 2 Word endings: ight	night, bright, right, light, fight, flight, knight, fright, tight, sight, might, slight, height, freight, eight, straight
Set 16 Sheets A, B & C	Year 4 Term 2 Word endings: tion, ious	station, ration, competition, question, action, reaction, information, subtraction, serious, ferocious, obvious, previous, curious, glorious, delicious, suspicious
Set 17 Sheets A, B & C	Year 4 Term 2 Common word endings	through, plough, cough, rough, enough, would, could, should, thought, brought, bought, drought, found, round, ground, sound
Set 18 Sheets A, B & C	Year 4 Term 2 Prefix: a	way, away, ground, aground, sleep, asleep, wake, awake, glow, aglow, live, alive, woke, awoke, long, along
Set 19 Sheets A, B & C	Year 4 Term 2 Prefix: ad	verb, adverb, apt, adapt, venture, adventure, join, adjoin, admit, adjust, advert, addition, admire, adopt, address, advance
Set 20 Sheets A, B & C	Year 4 Term 2 Prefix: al	ways, always, arm, alarm, so, also, most, almost, one, alone, ready, already, together, altogether, though, although
Set 21 Sheets A, B & C	Year 4 Term 2 Prefixes: ass, aff, att	assemble, assembly, assist, assistant, assort, assortment, attract, attractive, attend, attendance, affix, affirm, afflict, affliction, affection, affectionate.
Set 22 Sheets A, B & C	Year 4 Term 2 Prefix: a	aside, akin, aslope, ashore, astern, astray, astride, alert, avenue, avoid, await, afire, afar, afoot, afresh, again
Set 23 Sheets A, B & C	Year 4 Term 2 Consolidation and revision	bright, flight, alone, aloft, attract, admire, again, ascend, avenue, special, station, enough, subtraction, correction, through, suspicious

Year 4, Term 3 includes some words that have been seen before but are revisited and revised. Set 29, for example, returns to some of the words seen in Set 17. You may like to extend the children's examination of these words by asking them to think of as many words as they can which are spelt with ough, then to sort these words into groups according to the sound that this letter string makes: 'off', 'uff', 'oo', 'ow', 'u', 'oh'. Set 39 provides the opportunity to notice that the sion ending normally makes a 'zhun' sound, whereas tion makes a 'shun' sound - which two words in the set of sion words do not follow this rule? Such opportunities abound throughout the sets of words. We hope that you enjoy working with them.

Set 24	Year 4 Term 3	it's, its, active, captive, forgive, motive, native, massive, expensive, relative, competitive, inquisitive, expansive, corrosive, decisive, attractive
Sheets A, B & C	its, it's, suffix ive	
Set 25	Year 4 Term 3	river, liver, diver, hover, novel, shovel, favourite, fever, five, lever, flavour, level, leave, television, develop, devote
Sheets A, B & C	Using v in words	
Set 26	Year 4 Term 3	broken, hockey, package, racket, trickle, chuckle, monkey, pike, rocket, wrinkle, sticker, ticket, chicken, pickle, tickle, wicket
Sheets A, B & C	Using k in words	
Set 27	Year 4 Term 3	water, wave, wander, wall, swan, inward, swallow, beware, woman, worm, worry, world, swoop, swoon, sword, swollen
Sheets A, B & C	wa and wo	
Set 28	Year 4 Term 3	mission, impossible, missile, hassle, passion, passive, lesson, session, pass, fuss, process, guess, kiss, impress, boss, hiss
Sheets A, B & C	ss	
Set 29	Year 4 Term 3	tough, trough, thorough, though, bough, cough, through, thought, ear, hear, bear, tear, heart, earn, near, year
Sheets A, B & C	ough and ear	
Set 30	Year 4 Term 3	night, bright, slight, eight, weight, straight, freight, height, nice, rice, spice, dice, twice, mice, police, notice
Sheets A, B & C	ight and ice	
Set 31	Year 4 Term 3	trouble, found, around, journey, route, pour, four, young, taught, caught, aunt, autumn, haunt, cause, because, sausage
Sheets A, B & C	ou and au	
Set 32	Year 4 Term 3	advent, invent, prevent, adventure, geography, geometry, geology, geologist, spectacle, spectator, spectrum, spectre, interact, interfere, intervene, interrupt
Sheets A, B & C	Common word roots	
Set 33	Year 4 Term 3	can't, didn't, don't, I'm, morning, often, first, much, being, change, coming, number, only, both, high, such, show, walk, turn, different
Sheets A, B & C	Useful words	
Set 34	Year 4 Term 3	outside, sometimes, without, birthday, something, someone, somewhere, somehow, cupboard, blackboard, fireplace, footwear, anything, everybody, beforehand, another
Sheets A, B & C	Compound words	
Set 35	Year 4 Term 3	microscope, microbe, micron, microphone, minibus, mini-beast, minicab, miniature, minimum, minimize, little, minor, small, tiny, petite, minute
Sheets A, B & C	Words connected to small	
Set 36	Year 4 Term 3	sudden, suddenly, second, secondly, hope, hoping, hopeful, hopefully, decorate, decorative, decoration, wonderful, wonderfully, beauty, beautiful, beautifully
Sheets A, B & C	Extending words	
Set 37	Year 4 Term 3	above, below, inside, outside, under, across, following, place, started, stopped, today, tomorrow, yesterday, never, where, until
Sheets A, B & C	Useful words	
Set 38	Year 4 Term 3	possible, impossible, reversible, terrible, horrible, edible, responsible, indestructible, passable, impassable, laughable, enjoyable, valuable, breakable, agreeable, miserable
Sheets A, B & C	ible and able	
Set 39	Year 4 Term 3	prevention, detention, invention, punctuation, communication, relation, conservation, multiplication, revision, invasion, tension, division, explosion, decision, extension, confusion
Sheets A, B & C	tion and sion	
Set 40	Year 4 Term 3	know, knew, watch, catch, opened, closed, begin, began, right, write, between, upon, while, different, during, used
Sheets A, B & C	Revision	

● Using the suffixes ment and ness.

Sheet
A
For use
with OHP,
for display
or
to make
matching
cards.

YEAR
4
Term
1

SET
1
Sheet
A

sadness	kindness
silliness	happiness
drowsiness	darkness
softness	hardness
agreement	appointment
merriment	enjoyment
entertainment	engagement
government	endearment

When a word ends with a y, change y to i before adding **ness** or **ment**.

However, if the y follows a vowel you can leave it alone.

Look: happy → happiness   employ → employment

Add **ment** or **ness** to each of these words to make new words.

merry → merriment

sad

dark

engage

hard

kind

entertain

govern

silly → silliness

drowsy

endear

soft

happy

agree

appoint

enjoy

Use the dictionary to help you to write a definition for each of the following words:

endearment   government   appointment

fold line

3. Copy each word in your best handwriting.

4. Look again at the first word, then fold the paper over it to cover it.

1. Look carefully at each word.

2. Say the word out loud.

5. Write the word in COLUMN 3.

6. Check your spelling.

7. Now do the same for each word.

Learn, Write, Check.

Name:

Date:

LEARN THE WORD	WRITE THEN COVER	WRITE THEN CHECK
sadness		
kindness		
silliness		
happiness		
drowsiness		
darkness		
softness		
hardness		
agreement		
appointment		
merriment		
enjoyment		
entertainment		
engagement		
government		
endearment		

Sheet
A
For use
with OHP,
or display
or
to make
matching
cards.

● Using the suffixes al, ic and ary.

music	magic
picnic	logic
fantastic	library
canary	dictionary
contrary	literary
medical	hospital
mystical	chemical
seasonal	traditional

Some words can have suffixes added to the end to make new words. For example, we can add the suffix **al** to the word 'music'.

Some words have suffixes that can be removed. For example, we can remove **al** from 'musical'. But the word 'music' already has the suffix **ic** as part of the word, and we cannot remove it. Try it!

The **ic** family have a family shield that shows their interests and talents. Illustrate their shield for them and make up a family motto.

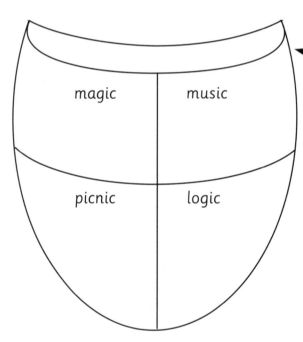

magic | music

picnic | logic

Write the motto in this space. You could include the word 'fantastic'.

On the other side of the paper, or in your exercise book, draw a shield for the **ary** family. Can you think of a motto for them?

Add the **al** suffix to these words and write them in your book or on the back of this sheet:

magic   music   mystic   logic

Write a sentence for each of the new words you have made.

fold line

Learn, Write, Check.

1. Look carefully at each word.

2. Say the word out loud.

3. Copy each word in your best handwriting.

4. Look again at the first word, then fold the paper over it to cover it.

5. Write the word in COLUMN 3.

6. Check your spelling.

7. Now do the same for each word.

Name:

Date:

LEARN THE WORD	WRITE THEN COVER	WRITE THEN CHECK
music		
magic		
picnic		
logic		
fantastic		
library		
canary		
dictionary		
contrary		
literary		
medical		
hospital		
mystical		
chemical		
seasonal		
traditional		

Sheet
A
For use
with OHP,
for display
or
to make
matching
cards.

kettle

kitten

dinner

riddle

little

woollen

better

mirror

middle

bubble

rubble

summer

batter

tatter

tomorrow

scrabble

The English language has lots of words with double consonants.

The answers to this puzzle all have double consonants.

Choose from these spellings:

woollen   scrabble
middle   kettle
mirror   bubbles
little   tattoo
summer   better
battery   riddle
kitten   rubble
dinner   tomorrow

Clues Across:

1. A season.
2. This provides electricity.
4. Polly put the_____on.
6. The day after today.
7. Centre.
8. A meal.
11. Good, _____, best.
12. Small pieces of brick and stone.
13. Small.

Clues Down:

1. Word making game.
3. Skin decoration.
4. Young cat.
5. A sheep has a_____ fleece.
7. Reflecting surface.
9. A puzzling question.
10. Soapy water makes these.

Is it possible to make a **double letter** word for every consonant in the alphabet?
Try it and see.
Which double consonants are never found in any words?

fold line

3. Copy each word in your best handwriting.

4. Look again at the first word, then fold the paper over it to cover it.

5. Write the word in COLUMN 3.

6. Check your spelling.

7. Now do the same for each word.

Learn, Write, Check.

Name:

Date:

1. Look carefully at each word.

2. Say the word out loud.

LEARN THE WORD	WRITE THEN COVER	WRITE THEN CHECK
kettle		
kitten		
dinner		
riddle		
little		
woollen		
better		
mirror		
middle		
bubble		
rubble		
summer		
batter		
tatter		
tomorrow		
scrabble		

Sheet
A
For use
with OHP,
or display
or
to make
matching
cards.

to	two
too	there
they're	their
night	knight
pear	pair
ate	eight
stare	stair
see	sea

Some words can sound the same, but are spelt differently and mean different things.

These words are called homophones.

Here are some examples of homophones:
to (I am going to...)
two (the number)
too (also)

Illustrate the following words to show that you know what they mean.

night	knight

pear	pair

stare	stair

see	sea

Use the following words in three sentences and write them in your book or on the back of this sheet.

    a)   there (a place)
    b)   their (belonging to)
    c)   they're (they are)

Try to find five more pairs of words that sound the same but are spelt differently. Can you illustrate them?

fold line

3. Copy each word in your best handwriting.

4. Look again at the first word, then fold the paper over it to cover it.

Learn, Write, Check.

1. Look carefully at each word.

2. Say the word out loud.

5. Write the word in COLUMN 3.

6. Check your spelling.

7. Now do the same for each word.

Name:

Date:

LEARN THE WORD	WRITE THEN COVER	WRITE THEN CHECK
to		
two		
too		
there		
they're		
their		
night		
knight		
pear		
pair		
ate		
eight		
stare		
stair		
see		
sea		

Sheet
A
For use
with OHP,
for display
or
to make
matching
cards.

brotherhood	knighthood
livelihood	neighbourhood
childhood	falsehood
friendship	membership
relationship	hardship
companionship	partnership
workmanship	craftsmanship
championship	ownership

The suffixes **hood** and **ship** are often found on the ends of words.

Remember, if a word ends in y change it to i before adding **ship** or **hood**.

Add the correct suffix to these words.

brother	➡	brotherhood	champion	➡	
knight	➡		lively	➡	
friend	➡		child	➡	
neighbour	➡		owner	➡	
relation	➡		partner	➡	

Follow the clues to find a **friendly** word down the middle of this puzzle.

Clues Across

1. Feline.
2. Bed for a baby.
3. A morsel.
4. A teapot has one.
5. Do this to potato.
6. Opposite of over.
7. Opposite of out.
8. Canine.
9. Spend this.
10. Travel on this.
11. Lives in water.
12. A light fog.
13. Opposite of down.

Choose from these words to answer the clues:

up,   bus,   cot

spout,   under

in,   cat,   mash

crumb,   money

dog,   fish,   mist

Work with a partner to see how many words you can find ending with **hood** or **ship**.

fold line

1. Look carefully at each word.

2. Say the word out loud.

3. Copy each word in your best handwriting.

4. Look again at the first word, then fold the paper over it to cover it.

5. Write the word in COLUMN 3.

6. Check your spelling.

7. Now do the same for each word.

Learn, Write, Check.

Name:

Date:

LEARN THE WORD	WRITE THEN COVER	WRITE THEN CHECK
brotherhood		
knighthood		
livelihood		
neighbourhood		
childhood		
falsehood		
friendship		
membership		
relationship		
hardship		
companionship		
partnership		
workmanship		
craftsmanship		
championship		
ownership		

Sheet
A
For use
with OHP,
or display
or
to make
matching
cards.

look	looks
looked	looking
stay	stays
stayed	staying
rush	rushes
rushed	rushing
wash	washes
washed	washing

Most verbs are doing words.

We change the endings of verbs for different uses.

For example: play, plays, played, playing.

1. Use the correct ending for the verb <u>look</u>, in these sentences:

a) Yesterday I [_____] for a new book to read.

b) The weather [_____] fine today.

c) I am [_____] out of my window.

2. Use the correct endings for the verb <u>stay</u> in these sentences:

a) I am [_____] indoors to keep warm.

b) The rabbit [_____] in a hutch last night.

c) My friend sometimes [_____] at my house in the holidays.

3. Use the correct endings for the verb <u>rush</u> in these sentences:

a) I [_____] home to tell my family the exciting news.

b) My dad [_____] to catch the bus each morning.

c) I am [_____] to finish my homework.

Make a set of three sentences for each of the following verbs and write them in your book or on the back of this sheet:

show (shows, showed, showing)
work (works, worked, working)
talk (talks, talked, talking)

fold line

3. Copy each word in your best handwriting.

4. Look again at the first word, then fold the paper over it to cover it.

5. Write the word in COLUMN 3.

6. Check your spelling.

7. Now do the same for each word.

Learn, Write, Check.

YEAR **4** Term **1**

SET **6** Sheet **C**

1. Look carefully at each word.

2. Say the word out loud.

Name:

Date:

LEARN THE WORD	WRITE THEN COVER	WRITE THEN CHECK
look		
looks		
looked		
looking		
stay		
stays		
stayed		
staying		
rush		
rushes		
rushed		
rushing		
wash		
washes		
washed		
washing		

● **Regular verb endings.**

stop	stopped
hop	hopping
drag	dragged
skip	skipping
carry	carries
carried	carrying
fry	fries
fried	frying

When a verb ends in a consonant with a vowel in front of it, we double the last letter when adding ing or ed.

Some of them end in y. You must change y to i when adding s or ed.

Complete these word patterns. One has been done for you.

Root word	s	ed	ing
knit	knits	knitted	knitting
stop			
		carried	
			skipping
hop			
	tries		
fry			
		dragged	
			crying

Try to write a verb (doing verb) for each letter of the alphabet.

eg: a = argue   b = buy   c = catch

Are there any letters that you cannot find a verb for?
Choose what you think might be an easy letter and find six verbs starting with that letter.
You may need a dictionary to help you.

fold line

3. Copy each word in your best handwriting.

4. Look again at the first word, then fold the paper over it to cover it.

5. Write the word in COLUMN 3.

6. Check your spelling.

7. Now do the same for each word.

Learn, Write, Check.

Name:

Date:

1. Look carefully at each word.

2. Say the word out loud.

LEARN THE WORD	WRITE THEN COVER	WRITE THEN CHECK
stop		
stopped		
hop		
hopping		
drag		
dragged		
skip		
skipping		
carry		
carries		
carried		
carrying		
fry		
fries		
fried		
frying		

Sheet
A
For use
with OHP,
or display
or
to make
matching
cards.

● **Irregular tense changes.**

go	went
buy	bought
bring	brought
eat	ate
run	ran
write	wrote
think	thought
fling	flung

When words change from the present tense into the past tense you often just add **ed**.

However, some words change quite differently when changing from the present to the past.

Look at the words in the word bank.
Sort them into two lists, a **now** list and a **then** list. The first two have been done for you.

WORD BANK

brought   go   thought   eat   flung   ran
         ate   bring   run   bought   buy
went   write   think   wrote   fling

NOW	THEN
run ⟶	ran

Write the past tense of the verbs below.
Sometimes it helps to try to think of a sentence which you can say in the present and in the past tenses. For example: I sing a song. I _____ a song.

sing   ask   swim   sting   leap   help   fly

3. Copy each word in your best handwriting.

4. Look again at the first word, then fold the paper over it to cover it.

5. Write the word in COLUMN 3.

6. Check your spelling.

7. Now do the same for each word.

1. Look carefully at each word.

2. Say the word out loud.

Learn, Write, Check.

Name:

Date:

LEARN THE WORD	WRITE THEN COVER	WRITE THEN CHECK
go		
went		
buy		
bought		
bring		
brought		
eat		
ate		
run		
ran		
write		
wrote		
think		
thought		
fling		
flung		

● **More irregular tense changes.**

Sheet
A
For use
with OHP,
for display
or
to make
matching
cards.

YEAR
4
Term
1

SET
9
Sheet
A

shoot	shot
catch	caught
fight	fought
hear	heard
shake	shook
wear	wore
creep	crept
break	broke

Here are some more words that have different ways of changing to the past tense.

Match each present tense word to the correct past tense word.

PRESENT TENSE
shoot   creep   (wear)
catch   hear   fight
break   shake

PAST TENSE
(wore)   shot   crept
caught   heard   fought
broke   shook

Now find the correct past tense words to fill these gaps.

One sunny day last summer, I enjoyed a walk in the woods. I [_____]

my new trainers and [_____] along the woodland path in them so

quietly that I [_____] sight of a squirrel sitting near the base of an

old tree. Unfortunately a twig [_____] under my foot and having

[_____] me, the squirrel [_____] off up into the branches.

The leaves [_____] as the small creature rushed through them. I

picked up an old branch and [_____] an imaginary battle before

returning home tired and hungry.

See if you can write a short story in the past tense.
Underline the verbs (doing words) you have used.

fold line

Learn, Write, Check.

3. Copy each word in your best handwriting.

4. Look again at the first word, then fold the paper over it to cover it.

5. Write the word in COLUMN 3.

6. Check your spelling.

7. Now do the same for each word.

1. Look carefully at each word.

2. Say the word out loud.

Name:

Date:

LEARN THE WORD	WRITE THEN COVER	WRITE THEN CHECK
shoot		
shot		
catch		
caught		
fight		
fought		
hear		
heard		
shake		
shook		
wear		
wore		
creep		
crept		
break		
broke		

Sheet
A
For use
with OHP,
or display
or
to make
matching
cards.

● **Making nouns / adjectives into verbs.**

YEAR
4
Term
1

SET
10
Sheet
A

special	specialise
theory	theorise
personal	personalise
apology	apologise
note	notify
jolly	jollify
beauty	beautify
pure	purify

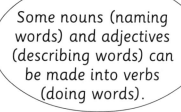

Some nouns (naming words) and adjectives (describing words) can be made into verbs (doing words).

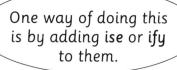

One way of doing this is by adding **ise** or **ify** to them.

Change the following words into verbs by adding **ise** or **ify**.
Remember you may need to change an **e** or a **y** at the end of a word into an **i**.

theory ⟶ [   ]   personal ⟶ [   ]

special ⟶ [   ]   apology ⟶ [   ]

ISE

IFY

note ⟶ [   ]   pure ⟶ [   ]

beauty ⟶ [   ]   jolly ⟶ [   ]

Now put your words into interesting sentences.

Try to write a sentence for each of the following words:

apologise   notify   personalised   classify   realise

fold line

1. Look carefully at each word.

2. Say the word out loud.

3. Copy each word in your best handwriting.

4. Look again at the first word, then fold the paper over it to cover it.

5. Write the word in COLUMN 3.

6. Check your spelling.

7. Now do the same for each word.

Learn, Write, Check.

Name:

Date:

LEARN THE WORD	WRITE THEN COVER	WRITE THEN CHECK
special		
specialise		
theory		
theorise		
personal		
personalise		
apology		
apologise		
note		
notify		
jolly		
jollify		
beauty		
beautify		
pure		
purify		

Sheet
A
For use
with OHP,
for display
or
to make
matching
cards.

flat

flatten

sweet

sweeten

tough

toughen

weak

weaken

awake

awaken

alien

alienate

elastic

elasticate

medicine

medicate

Some nouns (naming words) and adjectives (describing words) can be changed to verbs by adding **ate** or **en**.

Take care - the spellings of some root words change at the end before the suffix is added.

Look in the word search for the root words from the following verbs (for example, the root word for alienate is alien, so in the word search you are looking for **alien**):

alienate	elasticate	medicate	sweeten	flatten

awaken   toughen   weaken

START

C	D	L	F	P	P	E	A	W	O	O	B	A	S	S	R
F	E	T	I	C	A	E	C	R	A	W	A	K	E	L	T
S	L	E	E	M	D	I	R	P	Q	U	U	S	E	M	S
E	A	A	T	H	O	O	I	A	K	B	C	O	X	E	A
R	S	O	T	S	C	P	E	C	H	R	P	E	E	D	R
E	T	T	O	U	G	H	C	A	S	O	R	P	H	I	A
B	I	I	S	E	M	A	T	O	B	W	I	E	C	C	N
T	C	M	A	G	A	R	T	H	A	W	E	A	K	I	E
J	H	J	D	O	L	K	U	M	O	F	C	E	E	N	A
R	I	G	T	A	L	I	E	N	D	G	R	E	T	E	D

END

Moving from left to right on each row, write down the letter in every fourth square. Begin on the start square and finish on the end square. You will have found four more words ending in **ate**.

Use a dictionary to help you to write a definition for each of your new words.

fold line

3. Copy each word in your best handwriting.

4. Look again at the first word, then fold the paper over it to cover it.

5. Write the word in COLUMN 3.

6. Check your spelling.

7. Now do the same for each word.

Learn, Write, Check.

Name:

Date:

1. Look carefully at each word.

2. Say the word out loud.

LEARN THE WORD	WRITE THEN COVER	WRITE THEN CHECK
flat		
flatten		
sweet		
sweeten		
tough		
toughen		
weak		
weaken		
awake		
awaken		
alien		
alienate		
elastic		
elasticate		
medicine		
medicate		

Sheet
A
For use
with OHP,
or display
or
to make
matching
cards.

● **Consolidation of verbs and verb endings.**

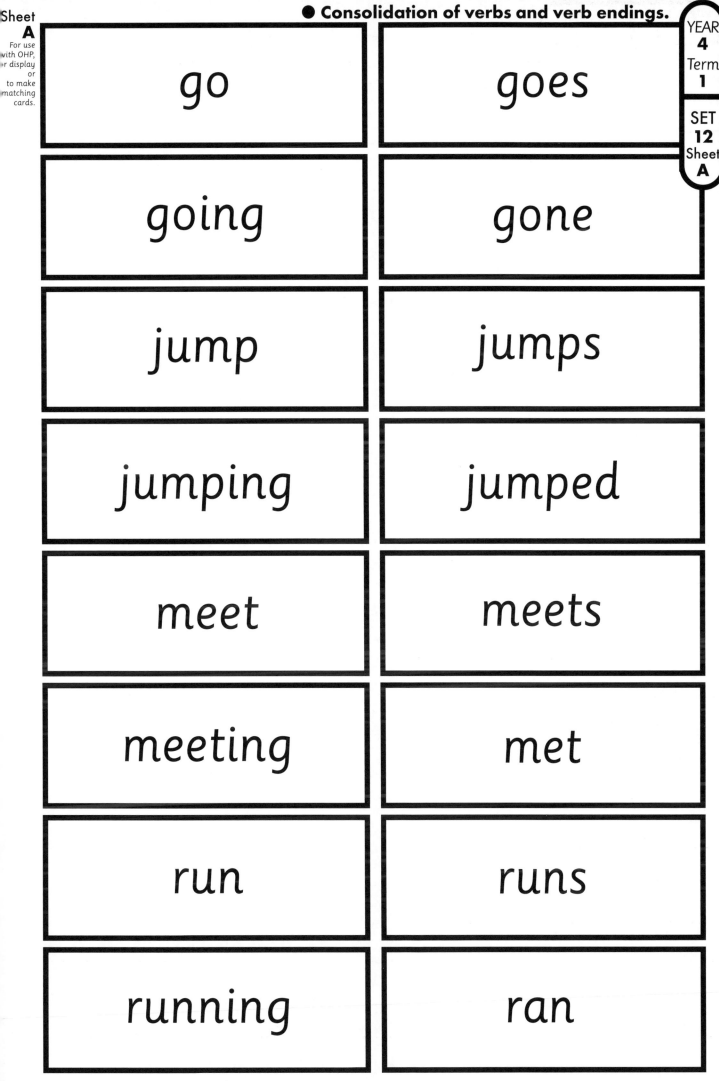

go	goes
going	gone
jump	jumps
jumping	jumped
meet	meets
meeting	met
run	runs
running	ran

Remember, verbs are doing words.

All sentences contain at least one verb.

Underline the verbs in the following passage:

My dog loves going out for very long walks. Her favourite is a good run along the beach. She barks fiercely at the crashing waves, and enjoys jumping in and out of the water. When we meet other dogs, she wags her tail and wants to stop and play with them.

How many verbs did you find? Write your verbs in the space below.

A game for two players:

Who can write down the most verbs in three minutes? See if any of your verbs are the same as your partner. Change the ending of each verb, eg: blow, blows, blowing, blew.

fold line

3. Copy each word in your best handwriting.

4. Look again at the first word, then fold the paper over it to cover it.

1. Look carefully at each word.

2. Say the word out loud.

5. Write the word in COLUMN 3.

6. Check your spelling.

7. Now do the same for each word.

Learn, Write, Check.

Name:

Date:

LEARN THE WORD	WRITE THEN COVER	WRITE THEN CHECK
go		
goes		
going		
gone		
jump		
jumps		
jumping		
jumped		
meet		
meets		
meeting		
met		
run		
runs		
running		
ran		

● **Revision and consolidation sheet.**

**Sheet
A**

For use
with OHP,
for display
or
to make
matching
cards.

YEAR
4
Term
1

SET
13
Sheet
A

amble

ambled

do

does

saunter

sauntered

tell

told

hair

hare

blue

blew

pedal

appointment

library

neighbourhood

You have learnt about spelling lots of different sorts of words this term.

This puzzle sheet will help you to remember all that you have learnt.

Puzzle 1 VERBS (doing words).

Sort out the words below into fast verbs and slow verbs. Take care, some of the words are not verbs and need to go in the last bag.

| amble | stroll | rush | quick | creep | shoot | saunter | turtle |

Ferrari   run   race   missile

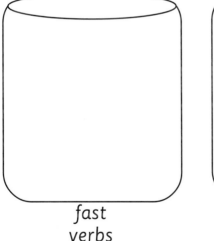

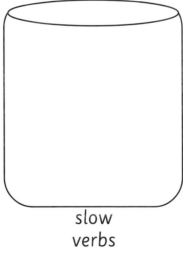

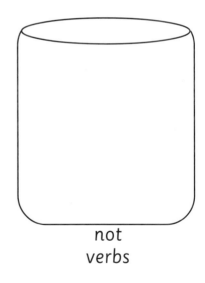

fast
verbs

slow
verbs

not
verbs

Puzzle 2 Follow the clues to find words with endings you have learnt this term.

The ending you will need is shown in brackets after the clue.

a)   To make something longer (en) _____

b)   A locality people live in (hood) _____

c)   A fixed place and time to meet someone (ment) _____

d)   A place that will lend you books (ary)   _____

e)   Put each foot on one of these when riding a bicycle (al) _____

fold line

Learn, Write, Check.

1. Look carefully at each word.

2. Say the word out loud.

3. Copy each word in your best handwriting.

4. Look again at the first word, then fold the paper over it to cover it.

5. Write the word in COLUMN 3.

6. Check your spelling.

7. Now do the same for each word.

Name:

Date:

LEARN THE WORD	WRITE THEN COVER	WRITE THEN CHECK
amble		
ambled		
do		
does		
saunter		
sauntered		
tell		
told		
hair		
hare		
blue		
blew		
pedal		
appointment		
library		
neighbourhood		

Sheet
A
For use
with OHP,
or display
or
to make
matching
cards.

● **Words ending in f, fe and ff.**

calf	calves
half	halves
self	selves
cliff	cliffs
sniff	sniffs
life	lives
knife	knives
safe	saves

Many singular words just have s added to make them plural.

Words ending with a single *f* or *fe* usually change to **ves** to become plurals.

The answer to all these clues are **plural** words. The box has some singular words to help you.

| glove | leaf | calf | half | wolf | knife |

These grow into cows   _____

Two equal pieces are   _____

These grow on trees   _____

Use these to cut things   _____

Wild animals, like dogs   _____

Wear these on your hands   _____

Now make up some clues of your own for the following words

_____   loaves

_____   scarves

_____   elves

Try to write down ten words ending in **ff** (double *f*). What happens when you make these words into plurals? With a friend, discuss what you have discovered.

Learn, Write, Check.

fold line

1. Look carefully at each word.

2. Say the word out loud.

3. Copy each word in your best handwriting.

4. Look again at the first word, then fold the paper over it to cover it.

5. Write the word in COLUMN 3.

6. Check your spelling.

7. Now do the same for each word.

Name:

Date:

LEARN THE WORD	WRITE THEN COVER	WRITE THEN CHECK
calf		
calves		
half		
halves		
self		
selves		
cliff		
cliffs		
sniff		
sniffs		
leaf		
leaves		
knife		
knives		
life		
lives		

YEAR
4
Term
2

SET
15
Sheet
A

Sheet
A
For use
with OHP,
for display
or
to make
matching
cards.

night	bright
right	light
fight	flight
knight	fright
tight	sight
might	slight
height	freight
eight	straight

When it follows a consonant **ight** sounds like **ite**.

But when it follows a vowel it sometimes sounds different. Try saying height, then weight. Different aren't they?

night	flight	tight	bright	fight	right
might	straight	knight	light	slight	fright

The answers to this puzzle are all **ight** words that are the opposites to the clues. The words in the box will help you.

day ⟶ ☐

loose ⟶ ☐

dull ⟶ ☐

dark ⟶ ☐

wrong ⟶ ☐

Use the correct **ight** words in the following sentences.

a) The _____ from London to Paris takes about an hour.

b) In days of old brave_____ would_____ with dragons.

c) I had a terrible_____ when the_____ went out,

and suddenly it was very dark.

In the boxes below, illustrate these **ight** words: eight, straight and freight.

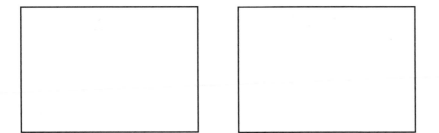

fold line

1. Look carefully at each word.

2. Say the word out loud.

3. Copy each word in your best handwriting.

4. Look again at the first word, then fold the paper over it to cover it.

5. Write the word in COLUMN 3.

6. Check your spelling.

7. Now do the same for each word.

Learn, Write, Check.

Name:

Date:

LEARN THE WORD	WRITE THEN COVER	WRITE THEN CHECK
night		
bright		
right		
light		
fight		
flight		
knight		
fright		
tight		
sight		
might		
slight		
height		
freight		
eight		
straight		

Sheet
A
For use
with OHP,
or display
or
to make
matching
cards.

● **Words ending in tion and ious.**

station	ration
competition	question
action	reaction
information	subtraction
serious	ferocious
obvious	previous
curious	glorious
delicious	suspicious

Many words end in tion...

...and many more end in ious.

Find the **tion** and **ious** words that have been put into the word bank. Write them in the correct safes and cross them out when you've found them.

WORD BANK				
station	learn	competition	obvious	to
spell	by	ferocious	looking	action
at	subtraction	your	suspicious	serious
glorious	word	previous	with	care
write	reaction	it	down	then
check	to	curious	ration	see
information	if	question	you	have
written	atrocious	it	correctly	delicious

word safe TION

word safe IOUS

Now, reading each line from left to right you will be able to write down some useful information from the words that are left.

Copy the following silly sentence in your best handwriting and illustrate it with care.

There was a lot of action at the station when the ferocious lion saw a delicious meal of people looking curiously at the information board.

fold line

1. Look carefully at each word.

2. Say the word out loud.

3. Copy each word in your best handwriting.

4. Look again at the first word, then fold the paper over it to cover it.

5. Write the word in COLUMN 3.

6. Check your spelling.

7. Now do the same for each word.

Learn, Write, Check.

YEAR 4 Term 2

SET 16 Sheet C

Name:

Date:

LEARN THE WORD	WRITE THEN COVER	WRITE THEN CHECK
station		
ration		
competition		
question		
action		
reaction		
information		
subtraction		
serious		
ferocious		
obvious		
previous		
curious		
glorious		
delicious		
suspicious		

● **Spelling words with common word endings.**

Sheet
A

For use
with OHP,
for display
or
to make
matching
cards.

YEAR
4
Term
2

SET
17
Sheet
A

found	round
ground	sound
could	would
should	cough
rough	enough
plough	through
thought	brought
bought	drought

Have you ever noticed how many words have **ou** in them?

The trouble with **ou** is that it can make different sounds, so you must look at those words with care.

Sort these words into the correct homes.

could	through	round	would	plough

drought   enough   brought   bought   found   should

thought   sound   cough   ground   rough

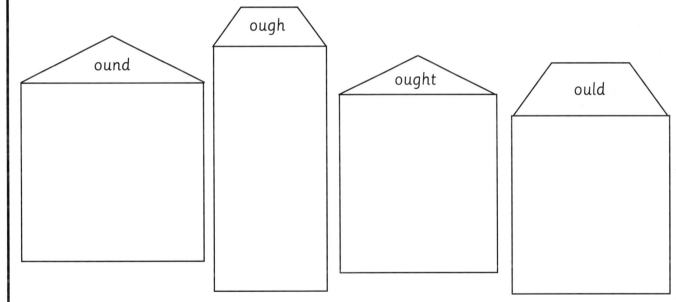

ound

ough

ought

ould

Read your words with care. Choose one word from each home to put into a sentence.

(ound) _____

(ough) _____

(ought) _____

(ould) _____

Write your own definition for eight of the sixteen **ou** words on this sheet.

fold line

3. Copy each word in your best handwriting.

4. Look again at the first word, then fold the paper over it to cover it.

5. Write the word in COLUMN 3.

6. Check your spelling.

7. Now do the same for each word.

Learn, Write, Check.

Name:

Date:

1. Look carefully at each word.

2. Say the word out loud.

LEARN THE WORD	WRITE THEN COVER	WRITE THEN CHECK
found		
round		
ground		
sound		
could		
would		
should		
cough		
rough		
enough		
plough		
through		
thought		
brought		
bought		
drought		

Sheet
A
For use
with OHP,
or display
or
to make
matching
cards.

way	away
ground	aground
sleep	asleep
wake	awake
glow	aglow
live	alive
long	along
woke	awoke

Using a as a prefix can slightly alter the meaning of a word.

For example, board can become aboard sleep can become asleep.

Follow the clues to solve the diamond puzzle. Use the words in the box to help you.

1. Ship a_____ the sailor shouted.
2. High up.
3. Getting on a ship or train is going a_____.
4. One more = a_____.
5. She was a_____ with jewels.
6. The ship ran a_____.
7. Not awake, a_____.
8. Not sleeping, a_____.
9. Go a_____.

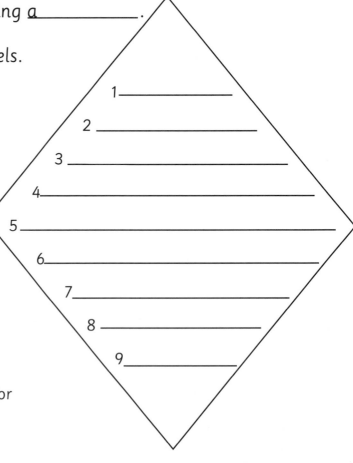

1 _____
2 _____
3 _____
4 _____
5 _____
6 _____
7 _____
8 _____
9 _____

WORD BANK

awake   aground   another
aboard   asleep   ahoy
away   aloft   aglitter

On the back of this sheet design a cover for each of these books:

'Life Aboard' by I. M. Afloat

'Another Astounding Tale' by Miss. Terry Writer

Now see if you can invent any more book titles with words which start with letter A. Try to think of interesting names for the authors too.

fold line

3. Copy each word in your best handwriting.

4. Look again at the first word, then fold the paper over it to cover it.

1. Look carefully at each word.

2. Say the word out loud.

5. Write the word in COLUMN 3.

6. Check your spelling.

7. Now do the same for each word.

Learn, Write, Check.

YEAR 4 Term 2

SET 18 Sheet C

Name:

Date:

LEARN THE WORD	WRITE THEN COVER	WRITE THEN CHECK
way		
away		
ground		
aground		
sleep		
asleep		
wake		
awake		
glow		
aglow		
live		
alive		
long		
along		
woke		
awoke		

Sheet
A
For use
with OHP,
for display
or
to make
matching
cards.

verb	adverb
apt	adapt
venture	adventure
join	adjoin
admit	adjust
advert	addition
admire	adopt
address	advance

The prefix **ad** sometimes alters words.

The prefix **ad** in front of a word usually means 'going towards'.

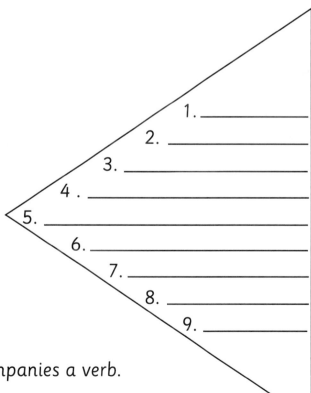

Triangular **ad** puzzle.
Follow the clues to solve the puzzle. Use the words in the box to help you.

adopt	advance	
adapt	adverb	address
adventure	adjust	
addition	admire	

1.   1. _____
2.   2. _____
3.   3. _____
4.   4. _____
5.   5. _____
6.   6. _____
7.   7. _____
8.   8. _____
9.   9. _____

1.   Take into a new family.
2.   Regard with pleasure.
3.   Go towards.
4.   Totalling numbers.
5.   A daring activity.
6.   To put in the correct position.
7.   Put this on an envelope.
8.   A word that sometimes accompanies a verb.
9.   To change something.

Write a definition for each of these words. Use a dictionary to help you.

admit   adjust   adjoin   advert

Learn, Write, Check.

fold line

1. Look carefully at each word.

2. Say the word out loud.

3. Copy each word in your best handwriting.

4. Look again at the first word, then fold the paper over it to cover it.

5. Write the word in COLUMN 3.

6. Check your spelling.

7. Now do the same for each word.

Name:

Date:

LEARN THE WORD	WRITE THEN COVER	WRITE THEN CHECK
verb		
adverb		
apt		
adapt		
venture		
adventure		
join		
adjoin		
admit		
adjust		
advert		
addition		
admire		
adopt		
address		
advance		

Sheet
A
For use
with OHP,
or display
or
to make
matching
cards.

● **The prefix al.**

YEAR
4
Term
2

SET
20
Sheet
A

ways	always
arm	alarm
so	also
most	almost
one	alone
together	altogether
ready	already
though	although

Another prefix is al.

It sometimes means 'the' or 'all'.

Follow the clues to solve the al triangle puzzle. Use the words in the box to help you.

almost   although   also
altogether   alone
already

1. As well.
2. By myself.
3. Nearly.
4. By this time.
5. Even though.
6. Totally.

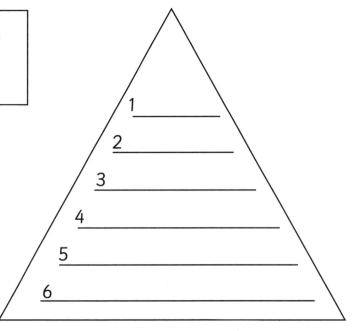

Write a definition for each of the following words. Use a dictionary to help you.

alarm   always   allure   allot

(Please note: allot is not the same thing as a lot)

Learn, Write, Check.

1. Look carefully at each word.

2. Say the word out loud.

3. Copy each word in your best handwriting.

4. Look again at the first word, then fold the paper over it to cover it.

5. Write the word in COLUMN 3.

6. Check your spelling.

7. Now do the same for each word.

fold line

Name:

Date:

LEARN THE WORD	WRITE THEN COVER	WRITE THEN CHECK
ways		
always		
arm		
alarm		
so		
also		
most		
almost		
one		
alone		
together		
altogether		
ready		
already		
though		
although		

Sheet
A
For use
with OHP,
for display
or
to make
matching
cards.

YEAR
4
Term
2

SET
21
Sheet
A

assemble	assembly
assist	assistant
assort	assortment
attract	attractive
attend	attendance
affix	affirm
afflict	affliction
affection	affectionate

When you have assembly …

… everybody assembles in the hall.

Try to fit the correct words into the sentences. The words that you will need are in the box.

attend	assemble	assortment	affliction	affectionate

1. There is a very good _____ of chocolates in the box.

2. My dog is a very _____ pet.

3. I _____ school every day.

4. The sick man was suffering from a dreadful _____ .

5. When the fire alarm sounds, we all _____ in the playground.

Use a dictionary to help you to write a definition for the following words:

affirm   attractive   attend   affix

fold line

3. Copy each word in your best handwriting.

4. Look again at the first word, then fold the paper over it to cover it.

1. Look carefully at each word.

2. Say the word out loud.

5. Write the word in COLUMN 3.

6. Check your spelling.

7. Now do the same for each word.

Learn, Write, Check.

Name:

Date:

LEARN THE WORD	WRITE THEN COVER	WRITE THEN CHECK
assemble		
assembly		
assist		
assistant		
assort		
assortment		
attract		
attractive		
attend		
attendance		
affix		
affirm		
afflict		
affliction		
affection		
affectionate		

Sheet
A
For use
with OHP,
display
or
to make
matching
cards.

● **Prefix a (a consolidation).**

aside	akin
aslope	ashore
astern	astray
astride	alert
avenue	avoid
await	afire
afar	afoot
afresh	again

Let's have another look at the prefix **a**.

Find the words with the prefix **a** in this puzzle.

Find and lightly colour the **a** words in this puzzle.
The words you are looking for are written below.
They may be horizontal ——→ vertical | or diagonal ↘

aside	astride	atonal	ashore	aloft	afresh
astray	astern	away	avenue	around	avoid
ahoy	alive	akin	await	afire	afar
	again	alert	aslope	afoot	

A	W	A	Y	A	T	B	H	U	A	T	O	N	A	L	Z	E	Z	A	P	B
U	R	Z	A	E	B	B	U	F	G	Z	Z	I	U	X	A	S	L	O	P	E
I	A	A	S	I	D	E	Z	Z	A	U	A	A	Z	S	U	B	Z	O	N	A
A	A	H	O	Y	A	A	A	F	I	R	E	Z	A	B	A	L	I	V	E	A
B	T	U	Z	A	H	B	U	Z	N	A	B	U	A	S	T	R	I	D	E	Z
A	B	A	A	B	U	Z	E	A	B	U	A	Z	S	A	B	U	Z	A	B	U
B	U	W	S	Z	F	A	B	U	R	Z	L	A	H	B	U	O	Z	Z	A	B
U	U	A	Z	T	A	B	A	B	A	B	O	A	O	B	B	A	L	E	R	T
Z	Z	I	Z	N	E	A	B	T	U	A	F	A	R	Z	Z	A	O	B	U	Z
A	B	T	Z	A	B	R	U	Z	F	Z	T	Z	E	Z	A	B	U	Z	Z	A
B	A	A	B	A	V	E	N	U	E	A	B	U	Z	A	U	A	A	U	B	Z
U	B	U	Z	B	U	Z	A	K	I	N	B	U	Z	T	B	A	V	A	H	Z
Z	A	F	R	E	S	H	A	B	A	F	O	O	T	A	B	Z	O	A	B	A
A	E	A	B	U	Z	A	W	B	U	Z	O	A	B	U	Z	Z	I	A	Z	Z
A	S	T	R	A	Y	A	B	A	R	O	U	N	D	A	R	B	D	B	D	Z

Now lightly colour all the extra letters: a, b, u and z.
Write down the remaining letters (reading from left to right on each line), and you will find a message.

Learn, Write, Check.

fold line

1. Look carefully at each word.

2. Say the word out loud.

3. Copy each word in your best handwriting.

4. Look again at the first word, then fold the paper over it to cover it.

5. Write the word in COLUMN 3.

6. Check your spelling.

7. Now do the same for each word.

Name:

Date:

LEARN THE WORD	WRITE THEN COVER	WRITE THEN CHECK
aside		
akin		
aslope		
ashore		
astern		
astray		
astride		
alert		
avenue		
avoid		
await		
afire		
afar		
afoot		
afresh		
again		

Sheet
A
For use
with OHP,
for display
or
to make
matching
cards.

bright	flight
alone	aloft
attract	admire
again	ascend
avenue	special
station	subtraction
correction	enough
through	suspicious

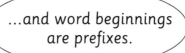

Word endings are called suffixes...

...and word beginnings are prefixes.

Sort these words and post them into the correct boxes.

correction	aloft	through	ascend	subtraction
suspicious	flight	avenue	alone	bright enough
station	attract	again	special	admire

af at as al

ad a

ight ough

ial tion ious

Find four more words that would go in each box.

fold line

3. Copy each word in your best handwriting.

4. Look again at the first word, then fold the paper over it to cover it.

5. Write the word in COLUMN 3.

6. Check your spelling.

7. Now do the same for each word.

Learn, Write, Check.

Name:

Date:

1. Look carefully at each word.

2. Say the word out loud.

LEARN THE WORD	WRITE THEN COVER	WRITE THEN CHECK
bright		
flight		
alone		
aloft		
attract		
admire		
again		
ascend		
avenue		
special		
station		
subtraction		
correction		
enough		
through		
suspicious		

Sheet
A
For use
with OHP,
or display
or
to make
matching
cards.

● its, it's and the suffix ive.

it's

its

active

captive

forgive

motive

native

massive

expensive

relative

competitive

inquisitive

expansive

corrosive

decisive

attractive

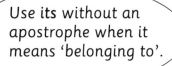

it's is short for it is.

Use its without an apostrophe when it means 'belonging to'.

See if you can put it's or its correctly in the following sentences.

1. The skipping rope had lost _____ handle.
2. I think _____ wonderful having a holiday.
3. _____ getting late so I should go home now.
4. The cat will defend _____ territory.
5. _____ a bright sunny day.

Now complete each of these sentences with a word ending in **ive**. The words you will need are in the box.

active	captive	competitive	relative	massive	expensive

1. Gold jewellery is very_____ .
2. A gymnast is very _____ .
3. A prisoner is a _____.
4. Something very large is _____ .
5. My uncle is a _____.
6. I like to win as I am very _____ .

fold line

3. Copy each word in your best handwriting.

4. Look again at the first word, then fold the paper over it to cover it.

5. Write the word in COLUMN 3.

6. Check your spelling.

7. Now do the same for each word.

Learn, Write, Check.

1. Look carefully at each word.

2. Say the word out loud.

Name:

Date:

LEARN THE WORD	WRITE THEN COVER	WRITE THEN CHECK
it's		
its		
active		
captive		
forgive		
motive		
native		
massive		
expensive		
relative		
competitive		
inquisitive		
expansive		
corrosive		
decisive		
attractive		

© Andrew Brodie *Publications* ✓ www.acblack.com

Sheet
A
For use
with OHP,
for display
or
to make
matching
cards.

river

liver

diver

hover

novel

shovel

favourite

fever

five

flavour

level

lever

leave

television

develop

devote

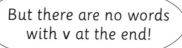

There are many words with **v** at the beginning or in the middle.

But there are no words with **v** at the end!

Are there any other letters that never occur at the ends of words?
Make a <u>word ending</u> alphabet to find out. It has been started for you.

A banana	J	S
B bulb	K	T
C	L	U
D	M	V
E	N	W
F	O	X
G	P	Y
H	Q	Z
I	R	

Which letters never occur at the end of English words? ☐ ☐ ☐

Write five words with z at the beginning, five with z in the middle and five with z at the end.

fold line

1. Look carefully at each word.

2. Say the word out loud.

3. Copy each word in your best handwriting.

4. Look again at the first word, then fold the paper over it to cover it.

5. Write the word in COLUMN 3.

6. Check your spelling.

7. Now do the same for each word.

Learn, Write, Check.

Name:

Date:

LEARN THE WORD	WRITE THEN COVER	WRITE THEN CHECK
river		
liver		
diver		
hover		
novel		
shovel		
favourite		
fever		
five		
flavour		
level		
lever		
leave		
television		
develop		
devote		

Sheet
A

For use
ith OHP,
display
or
to make
atching
cards.

● **Using k in words.**

YEAR
4
Term
3

SET
26
Sheet
A

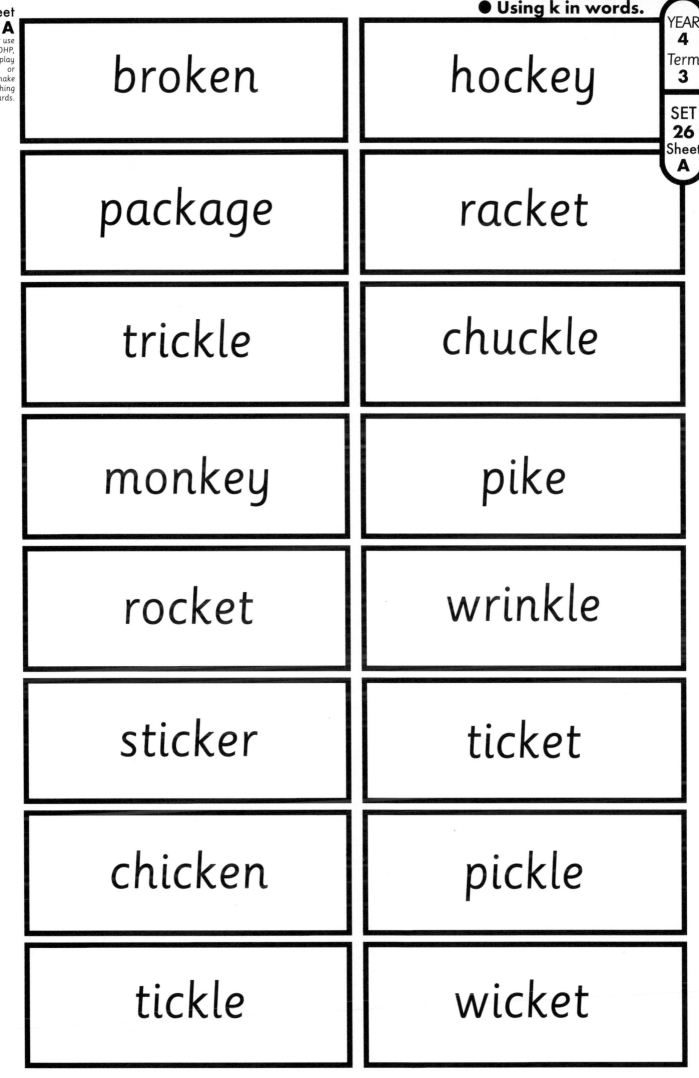

broken	hockey
package	racket
trickle	chuckle
monkey	pike
rocket	wrinkle
sticker	ticket
chicken	pickle
btickle	wicket

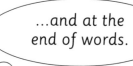

The letter **k** can be found at the start, in the middle ...

...and at the end of words.

Answer these clues correctly and you will find a noisy word down the left hand column. Use the words that are in the box.

1.
2.
3.
4.
5.
6.

chuckle	kettle	rocket
asked	tickle	elk

1. Go into space with this.
2. Requested
3. A type of laugh.
4. Boil water in this.
5. A deer like animal.
6. This might make you laugh.

The letter **k** is often found following **c**, eg: click, sack. Write 20 more words with **ck** in.

Are there any letters that are never followed by **k**? Investigate this with a friend.

fold line

1. Look carefully at each word.

2. Say the word out loud.

3. Copy each word in your best handwriting.

4. Look again at the first word, then fold the paper over it to cover it.

5. Write the word in COLUMN 3.

6. Check your spelling.

7. Now do the same for each word.

Learn, Write, Check.

YEAR
4
Term
3

SET
26
Sheet
C

Name:

Date:

LEARN THE WORD	WRITE THEN COVER	WRITE THEN CHECK
broken		
hockey		
package		
racket		
trickle		
chuckle		
monkey		
pike		
rocket		
wrinkle		
sticker		
ticket		
chicken		
pickle		
tickle		
wicket		

Sheet
A
For use
with OHP,
for display
or
to make
matching
cards.

water	wave
wander	wall
swan	inward
swallow	beware
woman	worm
worry	world
swoop	swoon
sword	swollen

The pairs of letters **wa** and **wo** are often found at the beginning of words.

They are also found in the middle of words, but very rarely at the ends of words.

Illustrate these book covers.

Famous Sword Swallowers

Life Under the Watery Waves

Building Wobbly Walls

Use a dictionary to help you to find at least 20 more words with **wo** or **wa**. Write the words you find in the space below.

Use your **wa** and **wo** words to invent some more interesting book titles. Illustrate your new book covers!

Learn, Write, Check.

1. Look carefully at each word.

2. Say the word out loud.

3. Copy each word in your best handwriting.

4. Look again at the first word, then fold the paper over it to cover it.

5. Write the word in COLUMN 3.

6. Check your spelling.

7. Now do the same for each word.

fold line

Name:

Date:

LEARN THE WORD	WRITE THEN COVER	WRITE THEN CHECK
water		
wave		
wander		
wall		
swan		
inward		
swallow		
beware		
woman		
worm		
worry		
world		
swoop		
swoon		
sword		
swollen		

Sheet
A
For use
with OHP,
or display
or
to make
matching
cards.

● **double s.**

YEAR
4
Term
3

SET
28
Sheet
A

mission	impossible
missile	hassle
passion	passive
lesson	session
pass	fuss
process	guess
kiss	impress
boss	hiss

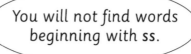

Many words have ss at the end or in the middle.

You will not find words beginning with ss.

Follow the clues to answer these word puzzles. The answers are all **ss** words. Use the words in the box to help you. Take care, there are more words in the box than you need!

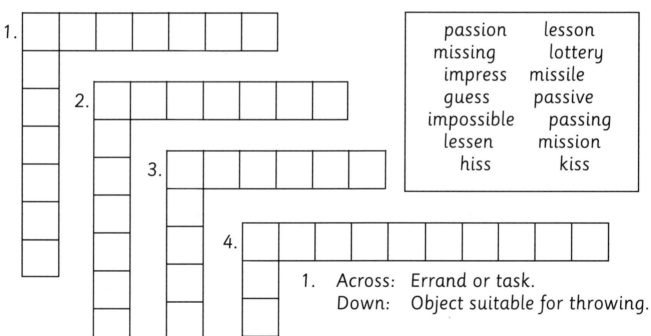

passion	lesson
missing	lottery
impress	missile
guess	passive
impossible	passing
lessen	mission
hiss	kiss

1. Across: Errand or task.
   Down: Object suitable for throwing.

2. Across: Not active.
   Down: Strong emotion.

3. Across: Learn this.
   Down: Decrease.

4. Across: This is not possible.
   Down: To make an impression.

Work with a partner. For each letter of the alphabet, try to find a word with ss in. Are there any letters that you cannot find an ss word for?

Learn, Write, Check.

fold line

1. Look carefully at each word.

2. Say the word out loud.

3. Copy each word in your best handwriting.

4. Look again at the first word, then fold the paper over it to cover it.

5. Write the word in COLUMN 3.

6. Check your spelling.

7. Now do the same for each word.

Name:

Date:

LEARN THE WORD	WRITE THEN COVER	WRITE THEN CHECK
mission		
impossible		
missile		
hassle		
passion		
passive		
lesson		
session		
pass		
fuss		
process		
guess		
kiss		
impress		
boss		
hiss		

● **ough and ear.**

Sheet
A
For use
with OHP,
for display
or
to make
matching
cards.

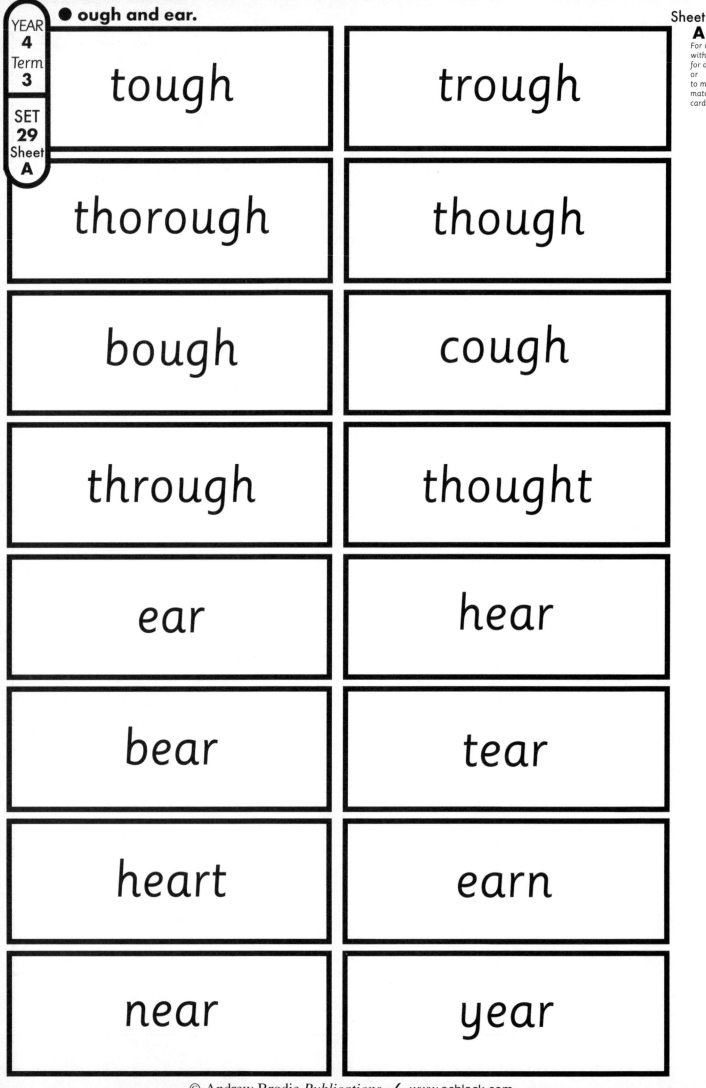

tough	trough
thorough	though
bough	cough
through	thought
ear	hear
bear	tear
heart	earn
tnear	year

The sounds **ear** and **ough** can make different sounds in different words.

For example, in the word **tear** the **ear** can say 'ear' or 'air' for different meanings.

A short clue and a rhyming word will help you to find the answers to the questions below. The solutions are all **ear** or **ough** words. The words you will need are all in the box.

trough	tough	tear	earn	bear	heart	ear	through

	clue	rhyming word	answer
1.	Found on the sides of a head.	beer	_____
2.	Pumps blood.	cart	_____
3.	Large furry animal.	hare	_____
4.	Difficult or chewy.	cuff	_____
5.	Holds food for animals.	cough	_____
6.	To work for payment.	burn	_____
7.	To go from end to end.	crew	_____
8.	To rip fabric.	air	_____

Put each of these words into an interesting sentence:

thought   thorough   though   year

weary   hear   near

fold line

3. Copy each word in your best handwriting.

4. Look again at the first word, then fold the paper over it to cover it.

5. Write the word in COLUMN 3.

6. Check your spelling.

7. Now do the same for each word.

1. Look carefully at each word.

2. Say the word out loud.

Learn, Write, Check.

Name:

Date:

LEARN THE WORD	WRITE THEN COVER	WRITE THEN CHECK
tough		
trough		
thorough		
though		
bough		
cough		
through		
thought		
ear		
hear		
bear		
tear		
heart		
earn		
near		
year		

Sheet
A
For use
with OHP,
or display
or
to make
matching
cards.

● **Letter strings ight and ice.**

night	bright
slight	eight
weight	straight
freight	height
nice	rice
spice	dice
twice	mice
police	notice

The letter string **ight** can also sound different in different words.

The letter string **ice** can sound like 'ice' in nice, like 'ees' in police and like 'iss' in notice.

Follow the clues to complete the word ring. The last letter of one word is the first letter of the next word. There are some words to choose from in the middle of the ring. You will need to turn the paper round to write the words in the ring.

1. A sudden shock might _____ you.
2. Opposite of day.
3. Double.
4. Tempt.
5. One more than seven.
6. Not loose.

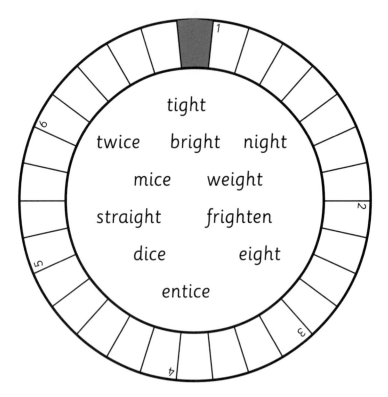

tight

twice   bright   night

mice   weight

straight   frighten

dice   eight

entice

Copy the following sentence in your best handwriting and illustrate it with care.

The policeman noticed the eight mice scurrying around near the sacks of rice and spices.

fold line

1. Look carefully at each word.

2. Say the word out loud.

3. Copy each word in your best handwriting.

4. Look again at the first word, then fold the paper over it to cover it.

5. Write the word in COLUMN 3.

6. Check your spelling.

7. Now do the same for each word.

Learn, Write, Check.

YEAR 4 Term 3

SET 30 Sheet C

Name:

Date:

LEARN THE WORD	WRITE THEN COVER	WRITE THEN CHECK
night		
bright		
slight		
eight		
weight		
straight		
freight		
height		
nice		
rice		
spice		
dice		
twice		
mice		
police		
notice		

Sheet
A
For use
with OHP,
for display
or
to make
matching
cards.

YEAR
4
Term
3

SET
31
Sheet
A

trouble	young
found	around
journey	route
pour	four
taught	caught
aunt	autumn
haunt	cause
because	sausage

The letter string **ou** can say 'or' or 'ow' or 'oo' or 'ur'. Try reading the words in the box which have ou in them.

Now look at the words which have got **au** in them. Does the au always sound the same?

Read this passage with care. Fill in the spaces with the correct words. The words you will need to use are in the box.

ground	sausage	through	thought
trousers poured	journey	autumn	aunt
because	favourite	route	

One warm _____ day my _____ decided to go for a

walk. She took her _____ _____ , past the football

_____ and _____ the shops. As she passed a cafe she

_____ she felt peckish so she ordered a cup of tea and a

_____ roll. The waiter tripped! The hot tea _____ all

over my aunt and the teapot fell to the _____ with a clatter. Her

_____ home was very hasty _____ she needed to put

on a dry jumper and some dry _____ .

Write ten more **au** words and ten more **ou** words. Include as many of them as you can in just four sentences. Read your sentences to a friend.

fold line

3. Copy each word in your best handwriting.

4. Look again at the first word, then fold the paper over it to cover it.

5. Write the word in COLUMN 3.

6. Check your spelling.

7. Now do the same for each word.

1. Look carefully at each word.

2. Say the word out loud.

Learn, Write, Check.

Name:

Date:

LEARN THE WORD	WRITE THEN COVER	WRITE THEN CHECK
trouble		
young		
found		
around		
journey		
route		
pour		
four		
taught		
caught		
aunt		
autumn		
haunt		
cause		
because		
sausage		

Sheet
A
For use
with OHP,
display
or
to make
matching
cards.

● **Common word roots.**

advent	invent
prevent	adventure
geography	geometry
geology	geologist
spectacle	spectator
spectrum	spectre
interact	interfere
intervene	interrupt

A word root helps
you to understand
the word.

The letter string **inter** is
a word root meaning
between.

Sort the words in the box into lists of the following roots:

vent   geo   spec   inter

spectator   spectre   adventure   geology   advent
interfere   geologist   interact   interrupt
spectrum   geometry   intervene   geography
prevent   invent   spectacle

vent	geo	spec	inter

Use the dictionary to help you to write a definition for each of the **geo** words.
What does the root **geo** mean?

3. Copy each word in your best handwriting.

4. Look again at the first word, then fold the paper over it to cover it.

1. Look carefully at each word.

2. Say the word out loud.

5. Write the word in COLUMN 3.

6. Check your spelling.

7. Now do the same for each word.

Learn, Write, Check.

YEAR **4** Term **3**

SET **32** Sheet **C**

Name:

Date:

LEARN THE WORD	WRITE THEN COVER	WRITE THEN CHECK
advent		
invent		
prevent		
adventure		
geography		
geometry		
geology		
geologist		
spectacle		
spectator		
spectrum		
spectre		
interact		
interfere		
intervene		
interrupt		

● **Useful words.**

YEAR
4
Term
3

SET
33
Sheet
A

Sheet
A
For use
with OHP,
for display
or
to make
matching
cards.

can't

don't

didn't

I'm

being

change

coming

number

morning

often

first

much

only

both

high

such

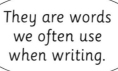

Here are some useful words.

They are words we often use when writing.

Arrange these useful words into alphabetical order.

can't	first	I'm	walk	high	different	being
such	coming	number	don't	morning	much	
turn	change	only	didn't	often	both	show

1._____   6._____   11._____   16._____

2._____   7._____   12._____   17._____

3._____   8._____   13._____   18._____

4._____   9._____   14._____   19._____

5._____   10._____   15._____   20._____

Complete this verb table.

ask	→	asking	→	asked
show				
come				
turn				

fold line

3. Copy each word in your best handwriting.

4. Look again at the first word, then fold the paper over it to cover it.

5. Write the word in COLUMN 3.

6. Check your spelling.

7. Now do the same for each word.

Learn, Write, Check.

Name:

Date:

1. Look carefully at each word.

2. Say the word out loud.

LEARN THE WORD	WRITE THEN COVER	WRITE THEN CHECK
can't		
don't		
didn't		
I'm		
being		
change		
coming		
number		
morning		
often		
first		
much		
only		
both		
high		
such		

Sheet
A
For use
with OHP,
or display
or
to make
matching
cards.

outside	sometimes
without	birthday
something	someone
somewhere	somehow
cupboard	blackboard
fireplace	anything
everybody	beforehand
footwear	another

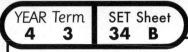

A compound word is made when two or more smaller words are put together.

Knowing this may help you to spell some of these words.

These 20 single words can be joined to make ten compound words.

out	shine	an	some	dust	sauce
other	bag	any	nut	cup	chest	pan	hand
bin	side	board	thing	sun	times

Write the compound words in the space below.

Complete these compound word chains. The first one is done for you.

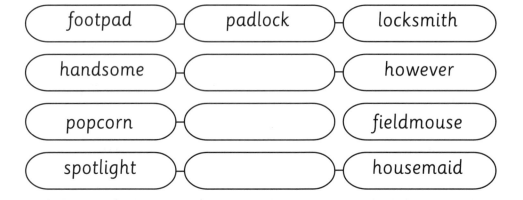

footpad — padlock — locksmith

handsome — — however

popcorn — — fieldmouse

spotlight — — housemaid

Try to find 20 more compound words. Use a dictionary to help you.

fold line

1. Look carefully at each word.

2. Say the word out loud.

3. Copy each word in your best handwriting.

4. Look again at the first word, then fold the paper over it to cover it.

5. Write the word in COLUMN 3.

6. Check your spelling.

7. Now do the same for each word.

Learn, Write, Check.

YEAR **4** Term **3**

SET **34** Sheet **C**

Name:

Date:

LEARN THE WORD	WRITE THEN COVER	WRITE THEN CHECK
outside		
sometimes		
without		
birthday		
something		
someone		
somewhere		
somehow		
cupboard		
blackboard		
fireplace		
anything		
everybody		
beforehand		
footwear		
another		

Sheet
A
For use
with OHP,
for display
or
to make
matching
cards.

microscope	microbe
micron	microphone
minibus	mini-beast
minicab	miniature
minimum	minimize
little	minor
small	tiny
petite	minute

Mini is a word root that means small.

Micro also means small.

Fill the blanks in the sentences below. The words you will need are all in the box.

microphone	miniature	microbe	minimum	minibus
	mini-beasts	microscope		

1. I would use a _____ to look at a _____ .
2. She sang into the _____ .
3. Look under a large stone to find some _____ .
4. Ten people went out in a _____.
5. 17 is the _____ age at which you can drive a car on the road.
6. A _____ poodle is a very small breed of dog.

Make a list of all the words you can find connected with small things, and a list of words to do with large things (eg: huge, gigantic, etc).

fold line

3. Copy each word in your best handwriting.

4. Look again at the first word, then fold the paper over it to cover it.

5. Write the word in COLUMN 3.

6. Check your spelling.

7. Now do the same for each word.

1. Look carefully at each word.

2. Say the word out loud.

Learn, Write, Check.

Name:

Date:

LEARN THE WORD	WRITE THEN COVER	WRITE THEN CHECK
microscope		
microbe		
micron		
microphone		
minibus		
mini-beast		
minicab		
miniature		
minimum		
minimize		
little		
minor		
small		
tiny		
petite		
minute		

Sheet
A
For use
ith OHP,
r display
or
to make
atching
cards.

● **Extending words.**

sudden	suddenly
second	secondly
hope	hoping
hopeful	hopefully
decorate	decorative
decoration	wonderful
wonderfully	beauty
beautiful	beautifully

Extending a word changes how we use it in a sentence.

Extending an adjective, by adding ly, can change it into an adverb.

Choose which form of each of the words in the box is best in the sentence.

decorate	decorative	decoration

1. I am going to _____ my room with colourful posters.

hope	hoping	hopeful	hopefully

2. The sailor was _____ he would not be seasick.

beauty	beautiful	beautifully

3. The painting was considered to be a thing of great _____ .

There are lots of endings which can be used to extend words. Here are some examples:

able   al   ic   tion   ly   ful   fully   less   ment   ist   ant   ity   ness   ive

Remember that sometimes we need to change part of a word to add an ending to it. For example, we lose the letter y from happy to make happiness.
See how many extended words you can make from the words below.

wonder   restore   care

You may need a big dictionary to help you!

fold line

1. Look carefully at each word.

2. Say the word out loud.

3. Copy each word in your best handwriting.

4. Look again at the first word, then fold the paper over it to cover it.

5. Write the word in COLUMN 3.

6. Check your spelling.

7. Now do the same for each word.

Learn, Write, Check.

YEAR 4 Term **3**

SET **36** Sheet **C**

Name:

Date:

LEARN THE WORD	WRITE THEN COVER	WRITE THEN CHECK
sudden		
suddenly		
second		
secondly		
hope		
hoping		
hopeful		
hopefully		
decorate		
decorative		
decoration		
wonderful		
wonderfully		
beauty		
beautiful		
beautifully		

© Andrew Brodie *Publications* ✓ www.acblack.com

● **Useful words to spell.**

above	below
inside	outside
under	across
following	place
started	stopped
today	tomorrow
yesterday	never
where	until

Look carefully at the list of useful words.

We use them a lot, so it is important to spell them correctly.

Useful words

above   inside   under   following   started

stopped   today   tomorrow   yesterday   where

until   never   place   across

outside   below

Write the word that is the opposite to the one given.

above   ⟶

inside   ⟶

over   ⟶

always   ⟶

started   ⟶

<u>Yesterday</u> a car <u>stopped</u> <u>outside</u> my house.

That sentence used three of the useful words. Write and illustrate three more sentences and try to put at least three of the useful words from this page in each one.

fold line

3. Copy each word in your best handwriting.

4. Look again at the first word, then fold the paper over it to cover it.

5. Write the word in COLUMN 3.

6. Check your spelling.

7. Now do the same for each word.

Learn, Write, Check.

Name:

Date:

1. Look carefully at each word.

2. Say the word out loud.

LEARN THE WORD	WRITE THEN COVER	WRITE THEN CHECK
above		
below		
inside		
outside		
under		
across		
following		
place		
started		
stopped		
today		
tomorrow		
yesterday		
never		
where		
until		

● **Suffixes ible and able.**

impossible	possible
reversible	terrible
horrible	edible
responsible	indestructible
passable	impassable
laughable	enjoyable
valuable	breakable
agreeable	miserable

We often meet the suffixes ible and able.

Remember - a suffix is a word ending.

Follow the clues to complete the words. If you do this correctly you will find an amazing word down the left hand column, spelt using the first letter of all your answers. Use the words in the box to help you.

climbable	enjoyable	impossible	indestructible
laughable	breakable	reversible	edible
notable	drinkable		

1. _____ No one could do this.
2. _____ Worthy of note.
3. _____ You can reach the top of this mountain.
4. _____ Can be worn either way out.
5. _____ Pleasurable.
6. _____ Good to drink.
7. _____ Cannot be broken.
8. _____ You can destroy this.
9. _____ Amusing / ridiculous.
10. _____ This will not poison you.

The amazing word that I found is: _____

For each letter of the alphabet find a word with either the suffix **ible** or **able**. The first two have been done for you.

a ➜ agreeable   b ➜ breakable

fold line

1. Look carefully at each word.

2. Say the word out loud.

3. Copy each word in your best handwriting.

4. Look again at the first word, then fold the paper over it to cover it.

5. Write the word in COLUMN 3.

6. Check your spelling.

7. Now do the same for each word.

Learn, Write, Check.

YEAR 4
Term 3

SET 38 Sheet C

Name:

Date:

LEARN THE WORD	WRITE THEN COVER	WRITE THEN CHECK
impossible		
possible		
reversible		
terrible		
horrible		
edible		
responsible		
indestructible		
passable		
impassable		
laughable		
enjoyable		
valuable		
breakable		
agreeable		
miserable		

Sheet
A
For use
with OHP,
for display
or
to make
matching
cards.

YEAR
4
Term
3

SET
39
Sheet
A

prevention

detention

invention

punctuation

communication

relation

conservation

multiplication

revision

invasion

tension

division

explosion

decision

extension

confusion

tion and sion are useful suffixes.

They change verbs (doing words) into nouns (naming words).

Put the **tion** and **sion** words into the correct word safes. Starting at the top and reading from left to right the remaining words will make an important message. Write out this message in the space under the safes.

WORD BANK			
please	prevention	revision	conservation
extension	tension	remember	invasion
that	these	confusion	suffixes
are	explosion	relation	able
punctuation	to	change	detention
division	verbs	decision	into
communication	invention	nouns	multiplication

word safe TION

word safe SION

Choose two **sion** words and two **tion** words. Put each of your words into a sentence.

fold line

Learn, Write, Check.

1. Look carefully at each word.

2. Say the word out loud.

3. Copy each word in your best handwriting.

4. Look again at the first word, then fold the paper over it to cover it.

5. Write the word in COLUMN 3.

6. Check your spelling.

7. Now do the same for each word.

Name:

Date:

LEARN THE WORD	WRITE THEN COVER	WRITE THEN CHECK
prevention		
detention		
invention		
punctuation		
communication		
relation		
conservation		
multiplication		
revision		
invasion		
tension		
division		
explosion		
decision		
extension		
confusion		

Sheet
A
For use
with OHP,
or display
or
to make
matching
cards.

● **Revision and useful words.**

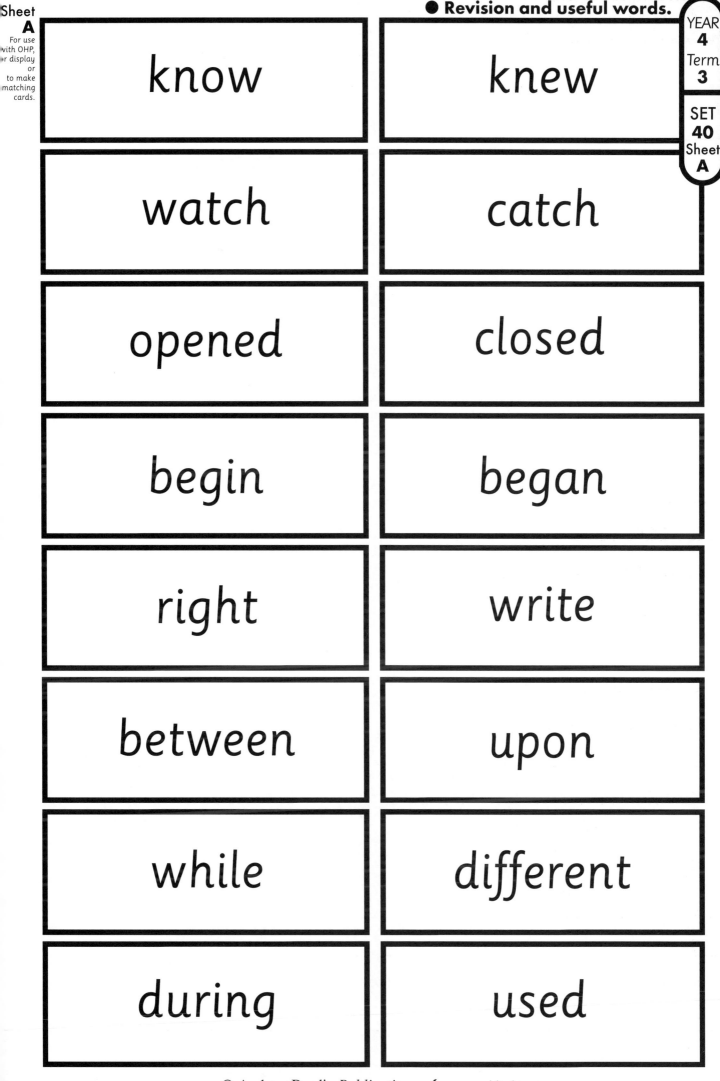

know

knew

watch

catch

opened

closed

begin

began

right

write

between

upon

while

different

during

used

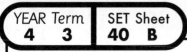

These are more very useful words.

Learn them with care.

Useful words

know	knew	watch	catch	opened
different	begin	began	right	between
write	upon while	closed	during	used

Find and shade in all the useful words in the word search below.

They may be horizontal ——→ vertical | or diagonal ⟍

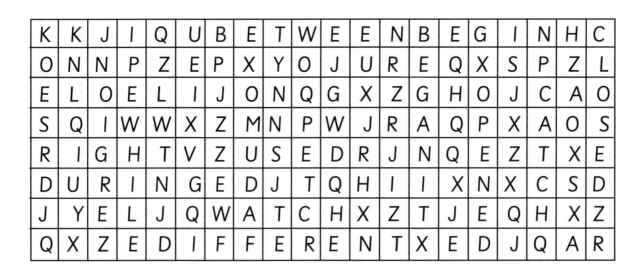

Now shade in all the extra letters J, Q, X and Z. Reading from the top, left to right you will find an important message. Write it in the space below.

fold line

3. Copy each word in your best handwriting.

4. Look again at the first word, then fold the paper over it to cover it.

1. Look carefully at each word.

2. Say the word out loud.

5. Write the word in COLUMN 3.

6. Check your spelling.

7. Now do the same for each word.

Learn, Write, Check.

Name:

Date:

LEARN THE WORD	WRITE THEN COVER	WRITE THEN CHECK
know		
knew		
watch		
catch		
opened		
closed		
begin		
began		
right		
write		
between		
upon		
while		
different		
during		
used		

ANSWERS

Some of the activities on Sheet B for each set of words require answers which are individual to the pupils. Some, however, have standard answers and we list these below to save time for teachers in marking pupils' work.

Set 1, Sheet B sadness, drowsiness, darkness, endearment, engagement, softness, hardness, happiness, kindness, agreement, entertainment, appointment, government, enjoyment.

Set 2, Sheet B magical, musical, mystical, logical

Set 3, Sheet B Answers across: 1. summer 2. battery 4. kettle 6. tomorrow 7. middle 8. dinner 11. better 12. rubble 13. little

Answers down: 1. scrabble 3. tattoo 4. kitten 5. woollen 7. mirror 9. riddle 10. bubbles

Consonants which never appear as double letters: h, j, k, q, v, w, x, y

Set 4, Sheet B Possible answers to last activity: sight, site   so, sew   hare, hair   cell, sell   pour, poor   sore, saw   blue, blew   toe, tow   write, right   lessen, lesson

Set 5, Sheet B championship, knighthood, livelihood, friendship, childhood, neighbourhood, ownership, relationship, partnership

Answers across: 1. cat 2. cot 3. crumb 4. spout 5. mash 6. under 7. in 8. dog 9. money 10. bus 11. fish 12. mist 13. up

Word down puzzle: companionship

Set 6, Sheet B 1. a) looked b) looks c) looking 2. a) staying b) stayed c) stays 3. a) rushed b) rushes c) rushing

Set 7, Sheet B stop, stops, stopped, stopping   carry, carries, carried, carrying
skip, skips, skipped, skipping   hop, hops, hopped, hopping
try, tries, tried, trying   fry, fries, fried, frying
drag, drags, dragged, dragging   cry, cries, cried, crying

Set 8, Sheet B NOW: bring,   go,   eat,   think,   write,   buy,   fling
THEN: brought,   went,   ate,   thought,   wrote,   bought,   flung
Past tenses: sang, asked, swam, stung, leapt (or leaped), helped, flew

Set 9, Sheet B cloze: wore, crept, caught, broke, heard, shot, shook, fought

Set 10, Sheet B theorise, personalise, specialise, apologise
notify, purify, beautify, jollify

Set 11, Sheet B

C	D	L	F	P	P	E	A	W	O	O	B	A	S	S	R
F	E	T	I	C	A	E	C	R	A	W	A	K	E	L	T
S	L	E	E	M	D	I	R	P	Q	U	U	S	E	M	S
E	A	A	T	H	O	O	I	A	K	B	C	O	X	E	A
R	S	O	T	S	C	P	E	C	H	R	P	E	E	D	R
E	T	T	O	U	G	H	C	A	S	O	R	P	H	I	A
B	I	I	S	E	M	A	T	O	B	W	I	E	C	C	N
T	C	M	A	G	A	R	T	H	A	W	E	A	K	I	E
J	H	J	D	O	L	K	U	M	O	F	C	E	E	N	A
R	I	G	T	A	L	I	E	N	D	G	R	E	T	E	D

Ringed letters spell: fabricate, rusticate, procrastinate, educate

© Andrew Brodie *Publications* ✓ www.acblack.com

Set 12, Sheet B Verbs: loves, going, run, barks, crashing, enjoys, jumping, meet, wags wants, stop, play

Set 13, Sheet B Fast verbs: rush, shoot, run, race Slow verbs: amble, stroll, creep, saunter
Not verbs: quick, turtle, Ferrari, missile
a) lengthen b) neighbourhood c) appointment d) library e) pedal

Set 14, Sheet B calves, halves, leaves, knives, wolves, gloves
Possible answers: huff, puff, stuff, snuff, buff, cuff, chuff, gruff, muff, cliff

Set 15, Sheet B night, tight, bright, light, right
a) flight b) knights, fight c) fright, light

Set 16, Sheet B TION: station, competition, action, subtraction, reaction, ration, information, question
IOUS: obvious, ferocious, suspicious, serious, glorious, previous, curious, atrocious, delicious
Words revealed state: learn to spell by looking at your word with care
write it down then check to see if you have written it correctly

Set 17, Sheet B ound: round, found, sound, ground
ough: through, plough, enough, cough, rough
ought: drought, brought, bought, thought,
ould: could, would, should

Set 18, Sheet B 1. ahoy 2. aloft 3. aboard 4. another 5. aglitter 6. aground
7. asleep 8. awake 9. away

Set 19, Sheet B 1. adopt 2. admire 3. advance 4. addition 5. adventure
6. adjust 7. address 8. adverb 9. adapt

Set 20, Sheet B 1. also 2. alone 3. almost 4. already 5. although 6. altogether

Set 21, Sheet B 1. assortment 2. affectionate 3. attend 4. affliction 5. assemble

Set 22, Sheet B

```
A W A Y A T B H U A T O N A L Z E Z A P B
U R Z A E B B U F G Z Z I U X A S L O P E
I A S I D E Z Z A U A A Z S U B Z O N A
A A H O Y A A A F I R E Z A B A L I V E A
B T U Z A H B U Z N A B U A S T R I D E Z
A B A A B U Z E A B U A Z S A B U Z A B U
B U W S Z F A B U R Z L A H B U O Z Z A B
U U A Z T A B A B A B O A O B B A L E R T
Z Z I Z N E A B T U A F A R Z Z A O B U Z
A B T Z A B R U Z F Z T Z E Z A B U Z Z A
B A A B A V E N U E A B U Z A U A A U B Z
U B U Z B U Z A K I N B U Z T B A V A H Z
Z A F R E S H A B A F O O T A B Z O A B A
A E A B U Z A W B U Z O A B U Z Z I A Z Z
A S T R A Y A B A R O U N D A R B D B D Z
```

The message says: THE PREFIX IS ON THE FRONT OF THE WORD

Set 23, Sheet B 1st box: ascend, alone, attract, aloft   2nd box: admire, again, avenue
3rd box: through, flight, bright, enough
4th box: correction, subtraction, suspicious, station, special

Set 24, Sheet B 1. its 2. it's 3. It's 4. its 5. It's
1. expensive 2. active 3. captive 4. massive 5. relative 6. competitive

Set 25, Sheet B Never at the end: J, Q, V   (though note that Iraq ends with a Q)

Set 26, Sheet B 1. rocket 2. asked 3. chuckle 4. kettle 5. elk 6. tickle Word: racket

Set 27, Sheet B Accept any recognisable words containing **wa** or **wo**.

Set 28, Sheet B Answers across: 1. mission 2. passive 3. lesson 4. impossible
Answers down: 1. missile 2. passion 3. lessen 4. impress

Set 29, Sheet B 1. ear 2. heart 3. bear 4. tough 5. trough 6. earn 7. through 8. tear

Set 30, Sheet B 1. frighten 2. night 3. twice 4. entice 5. eight 6. tight

Set 31, Sheet B autumn, aunt, favourite route, ground, through, thought, sausage, poured, ground, journey, because, trousers.

Set 32, Sheet B vent: adventure, advent, prevent, invent
geo: geology, geologist, geometry, geography
spec: spectator, spectre, spectrum, spectacle
inter: interfere, interact, interrupt, intervene

Set 33, Sheet B being, both, can't, change, coming, didn't, different, don't, first, high, I'm, morning, much, number, often, only, show, such, turn, walk
show, showing, showed come, coming, came turn, turning, turned

Set 34, Sheet B another, anything, chestnut, cupboard, dustbin, handbag, outside, saucepan sometimes, sunshine
Compound word chains: somehow, cornfield, lighthouse

Set 35, Sheet B 1. microscope, microbe 2. microphone 3. mini-beasts 4. minibus
5. minimum 6. miniature

Set 36, Sheet B 1. decorate 2. hoping 3. beauty
wonder: wonders, wondered, wonderful, wonderfully, wondering, wonderland, wonderment, wondrous, wondrously, wondrousness, wonder-struck
restore: restored, restoring, restorable, restorer, restores, restoration
care: caring, cared, cares, carefree, careful, carefully, careless, carelessly, carefulness, carelessness, caretaker, careworn

Set 37, Sheet B below, outside, under, never, stopped

Set 38, Sheet B 1. impossible 2. notable 3. climbable 4. reversible 5. enjoyable
6. drinkable 7. indestructible 8. breakable 9. laughable 10. edible
Word: incredible
Alphabet words - accept any that the children find that are recognisable words

Set 39, Sheet B TION: prevention, conservation, relation, punctuation, detention, communication, invention, multiplication
SION: revision, extension, tension, invasion, confusion, explosion, division, decision
Message: please remember that these suffixes are able to change verbs into nouns

Set 40, Sheet B

K	K	J	I	Q	U	B	E	T	W	E	E	N	B	E	G	I	N	H	C
O	N	P	Z	E	P	X	Y	O	J	U	R	E	Q	X	S	P	Z	L
E	L	O	E	L	I	J	O	N	Q	G	X	Z	G	H	O	J	C	A	O
S	Q	I	W	W	X	Z	M	N	P	W	J	R	A	Q	P	X	A	O	S
R	I	G	H	T	V	V	Z	U	S	E	D	R	J	N	Q	E	Z	T	X	E
D	U	R	I	N	G	E	D	J	T	Q	H	I	I	X	N	X	C	S	D
J	Y	E	L	J	Q	W	A	T	C	H	X	Z	T	J	E	Q	H	X	Z
Q	X	Z	E	D	I	F	F	E	R	E	N	T	X	E	D	J	Q	A	R

Message: I HOPE YOUR SPELLING HAS IMPROVED THIS YEAR